Fun With Mud
Diviértete con el barro

by Deborah Schecter

ISBN: 978-1-338-70278-1
Illustrated by Anne Kennedy
Copyright © 2020 by Deborah Schecter. All rights reserved.
Published by Scholastic Inc., 557 Broadway, New York, NY 10012

10 9 8 7 6   68   23 24 25 26/0

Printed in Jiaxing, China. First printing, June 2020.

■ SCHOLASTIC

Mud cookies.

Galletas de barro.

Mud cakes.

Pasteles de barro.

Mud pies.

Tortas de barro.

Mud donuts.

Rosquillas de barro.

Mud muffins.

Bizcochos de barro.

Mud bread.

Pan de barro.

Bake sale!

¡Venta de pasteles!